1 Animal Fair

4 I went to the animal fair,
The birds and the beasts were there,
2 The big baboon, by the light of the moon,
4 Was combing his auburn hair.

---

3 Are You Sleeping?

4 Are you sleeping,
Are you sleeping,
4 Brother John,
Brother John?
1 Morning bells are ringing,
Morning bells are ringing,
Ding dong ding.
Ding dong ding.

---

2 A-Tisket, A-Tasket

2 A-tisket, a-tasket,
A green and yellow basket,
2 I wrote a letter to my love,
3 And on the way I lost it.

(3) Auld Lang Syne

(3) Should auld acquaintance be forgot,
And never brought to mind?
(4) Should auld acquaintance be forgot,
And days of Auld Lang Syne?
(3)

(1) Baa, Baa, Black Sheep

(1) Baa, baa, black sheep, have you any wool?
Yes, sir, yes, sir, three bags full.
(4) One for the master and one for the dame,
And one for the little boy who lives
(3) down the lane.

(2) The Band Played On

(4) Casey would waltz with the strawberry blonde,
And the band played on.
(4) He'd glide 'cross the floor with the girl he adored,
(4) And the band played on.

(1) Be Kind to Your
(3) Web-Footed Friends

(4) Be kind to your web-footed friends,
For a duck may be somebody's mother.
(4) Be kind to your friends in the swamp,
Where the weather is always damp.

(4) A Bicycle Built For Two

(1) Daisy, Daisy, give me your answer, do!
I'm half crazy all for the love of you.
(1) It won't be a stylish marriage,
I can't afford a carriage,
(1) But you'll look sweet upon the seat
Of a bicycle built for two!

---

(1) B-I-N-G-O

(3) There was a farmer had a dog,
And Bingo was his name-o.
(1) B-I-N-G-O,
B-I-N-G-O,
(1) B-I-N-G-O,
And Bingo was his name-o.

---

(2) Boom, Boom, Ain't It Great
(3) to Be Crazy?

(2) Boom, boom, ain't it great to be crazy?
Boom, boom, ain't it great to be nuts like us?
(2) Silly and foolish all day long,
Boom, boom, ain't it great to be crazy?

(3) (4) Brahms' Lullaby

(4) Lullaby and good night, with roses bedight.
With lilies o'er spread is baby's wee bed.
(1) Lay you down now and rest,
May your slumber be blessed.
(1) Lay you down now and rest,
May your slumber be blessed.

(4) (3) Brother, Come and Dance With Me

(3) Brother, come and dance with me.
Both my hands I offer thee.
(4) Right foot first, left foot then,
Round about and back again.

(1) Camptown Races

(1) Camptown ladies sing this song,
Doo-dah, doo-dah.
(1) Camptown racetrack's five miles long,
Oh, the doo-dah day.
(2)

(2) Danny Boy

(2) Oh, Danny Boy, the pipes, the pipes are calling
(1) From glen to glen, and down the mountainside;
(1) The summer's gone, and all the roses falling,
(4) It's you, it's you must go and I must bide.

(3) Did You Ever See a Lassie?

(1) Did you ever see a lassie,
    A lassie, a lassie?
(4) Did you ever see a lassie,
    Go this way and that?
(1)

(4) Do Your Ears Hang Low?

(4) Do your ears hang low?
    Do they wobble to and fro?
(2) Can you tie 'em in a knot?
    Can you tie 'em in a bow?
(3) Can you throw 'em over your shoulder,
    Like a Continental soldier?
    Do your ears hang low?

7

① Down By the Station

④ Down by the station early in the morning,
④ See the little puffer bellies all in a row.
④ See the engine driver pull the little throttle.
④ Chug! Chug! Toot! Toot! Off we go!

---

② The Fairy Ship

④ I saw a ship a-sailing,
④ A-sailing on the sea.
④ And oh, it was a-laden
③ With pretty things for me.

---

③ Farmer in the Dell

② The farmer in the dell,
② The farmer in the dell,
④ Heigh-ho, the derry-oh,
① The farmer in the dell.

---

④ For He's a Jolly Good Fellow

① For he's a jolly good fellow,
① For he's a jolly good fellow,
④ For he's a jolly good fellow,
② Which nobody can deny.

① Found a Peanut

④ Found a peanut, found a peanut,
⠀⠀Found a peanut just now.
① Just now I found a peanut,
⠀⠀Found a peanut just now.
④

② A Froggie Went A-Courtin'

③ A froggie went a-courtin' and he did ride, uh-huh.
⠀⠀A froggie went a-courtin' and he did ride, uh-huh.
④ ⠀A froggie went a-courtin' and he did ride,
⠀⠀Sword and pistol by his side,
① ⠀⠀Uh-huh, uh-huh, uh-huh.

③ Girls and Boys, Come Out to Play

② Girls and boys, come out to play,
⠀⠀The moon is shining as bright as day.
③ Leave your supper and leave your sleep,
⠀⠀And come to your playfellows in the street.
②

9

(4) The Glow-Worm Song

(2) Shine, little glow-worm, glimmer! Glimmer!
(2) Shine, little glow-worm, glimmer! Glimmer!
(2)   Light the path, below, above, and lead us
(1)   on to love!

---

(1) Go Round and Round the Village

(1) Go round and round the village,
(1) Go round and round the village,
(2) Go round and round the village,
(4)   As we have done before.

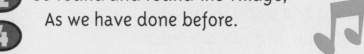

---

(2) Good Morning to You

(4) Good morning to you.
(4) Good morning to you.
(2)   Good morning, dear children.
(2) Good morning to you.

3 Good Night, Ladies

2 Good night, ladies.

1 Good night, ladies.

Good night, ladies.

2 We're going to leave you now.

---

4 The Green Grass Grew All Around

3 Now in a hole (now in a hole),

There was a tree (there was a tree),

4 The prettiest tree (the prettiest tree),

That you ever did see (that you ever did see).

2 The tree in a hole, and the hole in the ground,

And the green grass grew all around, all around,

And the green grass grew all around.

---

1 Hail! Hail! The Gang's All Here

3 Hail! Hail! The gang's all here.

Never mind the weather,

1 Here we are together.

Hail! Hail! The gang's all here.

2 We're sure glad that you're here too.

② ④ Head and Shoulders, Knees and Toes

④ Head and shoulders, knees and toes,
    Knees and toes.
② Head and shoulders, knees and toes,
    Knees and toes.
My eyes and ears and mouth and nose,
Head and shoulders, knees and toes,
    Knees and toes.

④ Here We Go, Looby Loo

① Here we go, looby loo.
    Here we go, looby light.
① Here we go, looby loo,
    All on a Saturday night.
②

③ ④ Here We Go Round the Mulberry Bush

① Here we go round the mulberry bush,
    The mulberry bush, the mulberry bush.
② Here we go round the mulberry bush,
    So early in the morning.

① Hickory Dickory Dock

① Hickory dickory dock,
     The mouse ran up the clock.
① The clock struck one,
     The mouse ran down,
③ Hickory dickory dock.

② Hippity Hop to
④ the Barber's Shop

④ Hippity hop to the barber's shop
     To buy a stick of candy.
① One for you and one for me,
     And one for sister Annie.

③ Home on the Range

④ Home, home on the range,
     Where the deer and the antelope play.
① Where seldom is heard a discouraging word,
     And the skies are not cloudy all day.
③

④ Home Sweet Home

② 'Mid pleasures and palaces though we may roam,
     Be it ever so humble,
② There's no place like home.
④

1 Hush, Little Baby

3 Hush, little baby, don't say a word.
    Mama's gonna buy you a mockingbird.
2 And if that mockingbird won't sing,
    Mama's gonna buy you a diamond ring.
4

---

2 I Had a Little Nut Tree

4 I had a little nut tree, nothing would it bear,
    But a silver nutmeg and a golden pear.
1 The King of Spain's daughter came to visit me,
    And all for the sake of my little nut tree.
2

---

3 I See the Moon

2 I see the moon,
    And the moon sees me.
2 The moon sees the somebody
    I'd like to see.
2

(4) (4) (4) (3) If You're Happy and You Know It

If you're happy and you know it, clap your hands.
If you're happy and you know it, clap your hands.
  If you're happy and you know it,
Then your face will surely show it.
  If you're happy and you know it, clap your hands.

(1) (3) (4) (3) I'm a Yankee Doodle Dandy

I'm a Yankee Doodle Dandy,
  A Yankee Doodle, do or die,
A real live nephew of my Uncle Sam's,
  Born on the Fourth of July.

(2) (4) (2) (4) Itsy Bitsy Spider

The itsy bitsy spider crawled up the water spout.
  Down came the rain and washed the spider out.
Out came the sun and dried up all the rain.
  The itsy bitsy spider went up the spout again.

15

(3) (2) I've Been Working on the Railroad

(1) I've been working on the railroad,
    All the livelong day.
(1) I've been working on the railroad,
    Just to pass the time away.
Can't you hear the whistle blowing,
    Rise up so early in the morn?
Can't you hear the captain shouting,
    "Dinah, blow your horn"?

(4) Jack and Jill

(4) Jack and Jill went up the hill
    To fetch a pail of water.
(1) Jack fell down and broke his crown,
    And Jill came tumbling after.
(2)

(1) Jimmie Crack Corn

(3) Jimmie crack corn, and I don't care.
Jimmie crack corn, and I don't care.
(1) Jimmie crack corn, and I don't care.
    My friend has gone away.
(3)

(2) John Jacob Jingleheimer Schmidt

(3) John Jacob Jingleheimer Schmidt,
(3)   His name is my name, too.
(3) Whenever we go out,
(3)   The people always shout,
(2) "There goes John Jacob Jingleheimer Schmidt!"

(3) Kookaburra

(3) Kookaburra sits in the old gum tree,
(3)   Merry, merry king of the bush is he.
(4) Laugh, Kookaburra! Laugh, Kookaburra!
(1)   Gay your life must be.

(4) Lavender's Blue

(4) Lavender's blue, dilly dilly,
(4)   Lavender's green.
(4) When I am king, dilly dilly,
(2)   You shall be queen.

(1) Lightly Row

(2) Lightly row, lightly row!
(2)   Over the glassy waves we go.
(2) Smoothly glide, smoothly glide
(2)   On the silent tide.

(2) Little Bo Peep

(4) Little Bo Peep has lost her sheep
    And can't tell where to find them.
(1) Leave them alone and they'll come home,
    Wagging their tails behind them.
(3)

(3) Little Boy Blue

(3) Little Boy Blue, come blow your horn.
    The sheep's in the meadow, the cow's in the corn.
(4) Where is the boy who looks after the sheep?
    He's under the haystack, fast asleep.
(4)

(4) London Bridge

(1) London Bridge is falling down,
    Falling down, falling down.
(3) London Bridge is falling down,
    My fair lady.
(2)

① Make New Friends

① Make new friends,
    But keep the old.
③ One is silver
    And the other is gold.
④

---

② The Man on the Flying Trapeze

② He'd fly through the air with the greatest of ease,
    A daring young man on the flying trapeze.
② His movements were graceful, adept as you please,
    And my love he has stolen away.
②

---

③ Mary Had a Little Lamb

① Mary had a little lamb,
    Little lamb, little lamb.
① Mary had a little lamb,
    Whose fleece was white as snow.
①

④ Mary, Mary, Quite Contrary

② Mary, Mary, quite contrary,
    How does your garden grow?
② With silver bells and cockle shells
③   And pretty maids all in a row.

① Muffin Man

④ Do you know the muffin man,
    The muffin man, the muffin man?
④ Do you know the muffin man
③   Who lives on Drury Lane?

② My Bonnie Lies Over the Ocean

④ My Bonnie lies over the ocean.
    My Bonnie lies over the sea.
③ My Bonnie lies over the ocean.
④   Oh, bring back my Bonnie to me.

The North Wind Does Blow

(3) The north wind does blow, and we will have snow,
(4)   And what will the robin do then, poor thing?
(4) He'll sit in the barn to keep himself warm,
(4)   And hide his head under his wing, poor thing!

Oats, Peas, Beans, and Barley Grow

(4)
(3)
(3) Oats, peas, beans, and barley grow.
(1) Oats, peas, beans, and barley grow.
(1)   Can you or I or anyone know
How oats, peas, beans, and barley grow?

Oh, Dear! What Can the Matter Be?

(1) Oh, dear! What can the matter be?
(3)   Dear, dear, what can the matter be?
(1) Oh, dear! What can the matter be?
(4)   Johnny's so long at the fair.

Oh, How Lovely Is the Evening

(2) Oh, how lovely is the evening, is the evening,
(4)   When the bells are sweetly ringing,
(3)   sweetly ringing.
(3) Ding, dong. Ding, dong. Ding, dong.

21

(3) Oh, Susanna

(4) Oh, Susanna,
  Oh, don't you cry for me.
(4) I come from Alabama,
  With a banjo on my knee.
(3)

---

(4) The Old Gray Mare

(4) The old gray mare just ain't what she used to be,
  Ain't what she used to be,
(4) Ain't what she used to be.
(1) The old gray mare just ain't what she used to be,
  Many long years ago.

---

(1) Old MacDonald

(1) Old MacDonald had a farm, E-I-E-I-O.
  And on that farm he had some chicks, E-I-E-I-O.
(1) With a peep-peep here, and a peep-peep there,
  Here a peep, there a peep,
(4) Everywhere a peep-peep.
  Old MacDonald had a farm, E-I-E-I-O.

② On Top of Old Smoky

① On top of Old Smoky,
 All covered in snow,
② I lost my true lover,
 From courting too slow.
①

③ One, Two, Buckle My Shoe

② One, two, buckle my shoe.
 Three, four, knock at the door.
③ Five, six, pick up sticks.
 Seven, eight, lay them straight.
① Nine, ten, do it again.

④ Pat-a-Cake

④ Pat-a-cake, pat-a-cake, baker's man,
 Bake me a cake as fast as you can.
② Pat it and shape it and mark it with "B,"
 And put it in the oven for baby and me.
②

23

① Pease Porridge Hot

④ Pease porridge hot,
　　Pease porridge cold,
④ Pease porridge in the pot,
　　Nine days old.
② Pease porridge hot,
　　Pease porridge cold,
　　Pease porridge in the pot,
　　Nine days old.

② Polly, Put the Kettle On

① Polly, put the kettle on.
① Polly, put the kettle on.
① Polly, put the kettle on.
② 　　We'll all have tea.

③ Polly-Wolly-Doodle

④ Oh, I went down South for to see my Sal,
　　Sing Polly-Wolly-Doodle all the day.
③ My Sal she is a spunky gal,
④ 　　Sing Polly-Wolly-Doodle all the day.

Pop! Goes the Weasel

(4)

(1) All around the cobbler's bench,
(1) The monkey chased the weasel.
(1) The monkey thought 'twas all in fun.
(3) Pop! Goes the weasel.

Rain, Rain, Go Away

(1)

(1) Rain, rain, go away.
Come again some other day.
(2) We want to go outside and play.
(1) Rain, rain, go away.

Rig-a-Jig-Jig

(2)

(1) Rig-a-jig-jig and away we go,
Away we go, away we go,
(3) Rig-a-jig-jig and away we go,
Heigh-ho, heigh-ho, heigh-ho.
(2)

Ring Around the Rosy

(3)

(3) Ring around the rosy,
A pocket full of posies.
(3) Ashes, ashes,
We all fall down.
(3)

25

Rock-a-Bye, Baby

Rock-a-bye, baby, on the treetop.
When the wind blows, the cradle will rock.
When the bough breaks, the cradle will fall.
And down will come baby, cradle and all.

Row, Row, Row Your Boat

Row, row, row your boat,
Gently down the stream.
Merrily, merrily, merrily, merrily,
Life is but a dream.

She'll Be Coming Round the Mountain

She'll be coming round the mountain
when she comes.
She'll be coming round the mountain
when she comes.
She'll be coming round the mountain,
She'll be coming round the mountain,
She'll be coming round the mountain
when she comes.

(3) Shortnin' Bread

(3) Mama's little baby loves shortnin', shortnin',
Mama's little baby loves shortnin' bread.
(2) Mama's little baby loves shortnin', shortnin',
(4) Mama's little baby loves shortnin' bread.

(4) Sing a Song of Sixpence

(4) Sing a song of sixpence, a pocket full of rye.
Four and twenty blackbirds baked in a pie!
(1) When the pie was opened, the birds began to sing.
(3) Wasn't that a dainty dish to set before the king?

(1) Six Little Ducks

(4) Six little ducks that once I knew,
Fat ones, skinny ones, fair ones, too.
(4) But the one little duck with a feather on its back,
(1) He led the others with a quack, quack, quack.

(2)
(4)
(3)
(2)
Skip to My Lou

Skip, skip, skip to my Lou,
Skip, skip, skip to my Lou,
Skip, skip, skip to my Lou,
 Skip to my Lou, my darlin'.

(3)
(4)
(4)
(2)
Smile and Show Your Dimple

Smile and show your dimple,
 You'll find it's very simple.
You can think of something comical,
 In a very little while.
Chase away the wrinkle,
 Sprinkle just a twinkle,
Light your face up,
 Just brace up, and smile!

(4)
(4)
(4)
(4)
Take Me Out to the Ball Game

Take me out to the ball game,
 Take me out to the crowd.
Buy me some peanuts and Cracker Jack®,
 I don't care if I never get back.
Let me root, root, root, for the home team,
 If they don't win it's a shame.
For it's one, two, three strikes you're out,
 At the old ball game.

Cracker Jack® is a registered trademark of Frito-Lay.

① Ta-Ra-Ra Boom-Der-Ay

③ Ta-ra-ra boom-der-ay, ta-ra-ra boom-der-ay,
③ Ta-ra-ra boom-der-ay, ta-ra-ra boom-der-ay,
③ Ta-ra-ra boom-der-ay, ta-ra-ra boom-der-ay,
① Ta-ra-ra boom-der-ay, ta-ra-ra boom-der-ay.

② Teddy Bear, Teddy Bear

④ Teddy bear, teddy bear, turn around.
 Teddy bear, teddy bear, touch the ground.
③ Teddy bear, teddy bear, tie your shoe,
 Teddy bear, teddy bear, I love you!
①

③ There's a Hole in the Bucket

④ There's a hole in the bucket, dear Liza, dear Liza.
 There's a hole in the bucket, dear Liza, a hole.
③ Then mend it, dear Henry, dear Henry, dear Henry.
 Then mend it, dear Henry, dear Henry, mend it.
③

④ This Old Man

① This old man, he played one,
 He played knick-knack on his thumb.
① With a knick-knack paddy whack,
 Give a dog a bone,
④ This old man came rolling home.

29

① Three Blind Mice

① Three blind mice, three blind mice,
  See how they run, see how they run!
② They all ran after the farmer's wife
  Who cut off their tails with a carving knife!
② Have you ever seen such a sight in your life
  As three blind mice?

---

② Three Little Kittens

① Three little kittens, they lost their mittens,
  And they began to cry,
① Oh, mother dear, we sadly fear,
  Our mittens we have lost.
③ What, lost your mittens? You naughty kittens!
  Then you shall have no pie.

---

③ Twinkle, Twinkle, Little Star

① Twinkle, twinkle, little star,
  How I wonder what you are,
② Up above the world so high
  Like a diamond in the sky!
① Twinkle, twinkle, little star,
  How I wonder what you are!